just time t...

I can't be...

Bible stories ... r 6–8s

Brian Ogden

Text copyright © 1999 Brian Ogden
Illustrations copyright © 1999 Adam Graff

The author asserts the moral right to
be identified as the author of this work

Published by
The Bible Reading Fellowship
Peter's Way, Sandy Lane West
Oxford OX4 5HG
ISBN 1 84101 051 0

First edition 1999
10 9 8 7 6 5 4 3 2 1 0

A catalogue record for this book is
available from the British Library

Printed and bound in Great Britain
by Caledonian International Book Manufacturing Ltd, Glasgow

Introduction

We all of us enjoy receiving letters and the children in Mr Green's class at Daisy Hill School are no exception. However, the letters they write and receive are a little different. The children correspond with some of the major biblical figures and, through the letters, begin to understand and associate with the events and personalities involved. Each book includes two Old Testament and three New Testament stories.

As Alex, not the best-behaved boy in the class, says: 'I never knew the Bible could be so exciting!' It is our hope and belief that your children will find the same as they read *I can't believe it!*

Contents

I can't believe it!

'There were,' said Mr Green, 'quite a lot of other very important things going on, round the time that Jesus was born. For instance, there was also the birth of his cousin. Can anyone tell me his name?'

As usual, it was Amy who knew the answer.

'I think it was John,' said Amy.

'Yes, well done. Jesus' cousin was John. When he grew up he was known as John the Baptist. His father was Zechariah and his mother was Elizabeth. Mary, Jesus' mother, went to see Elizabeth before both babies were born. But before that, something very unusual happened to Zechariah. He met an angel!'

'Wouldn't it be good if we could write to him and find out what happened?' whispered Alex.

'Good idea, Alex,' said Mr Green, whose hearing was better than Alex realized! 'I think you could write a letter to old Zechariah and find out how our story begins. I should address it to the temple in Jerusalem.'

Alex groaned loudly enough for the whole class to hear but started to write the letter.

And this is what he wrote...

Daisy Hill Primary School
Daisy Hill
DH6 7AB

Dear Mr Zechariah,

Our teacher, Mr Green, told us that something fantastic happened to you before your son John was born. Would you please write and tell us about it? Did you really meet an angel?

Best wishes,

Alex and 3G

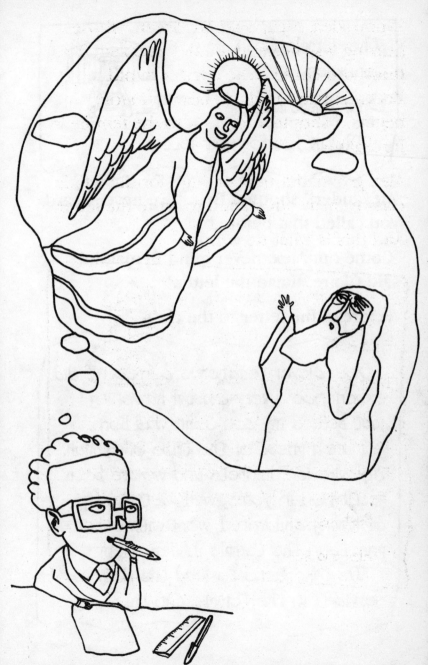

The Temple Court
Jerusalem

Dear Alexander,

Thank you for your letter.

'Alexander!' shouted Ben. 'I've never heard you called that before.'

'Come on, Alex, never mind Benjamin!' said Claire. 'Read the letter.'

Alex read the letter to the class.

Your clever teacher is correct. I did experience a very unusual happening just before my son John was born.

I am a priest of the tribe of Abijah. My wife is Elizabeth and we are both getting on in years, well past the age of having children. I work with other priests in the temple in Jerusalem.

We take turns to lead the daily services in the temple. On this particular day I was on my own inside the temple, getting ready to light the incense. People were outside waiting. Suddenly I knew there was someone else with me. I looked and saw an angel standing by the altar. It was God's messenger, Gabriel—the same messenger who visited Mary, the mother of Jesus, as I learned later.

I must go. It's service time and I am on duty.

May the Lord bless you as he has blessed me,

Zechariah

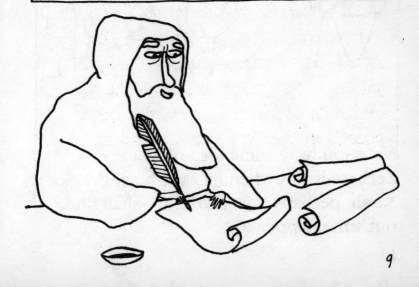

'But he never told us what happened,' complained Sarah. 'I mean, he said he saw the angel, but what did the angel say?'

'Perhaps you'd like to write and find out,' suggested Mr Green. 'But before you do, I think we'll look at this picture of the temple in Jerusalem.

Now you have some idea of where Zechariah was when he saw the angel. So Sarah, perhaps if you write we shall find out what happened.'

And this is what Sarah wrote…

Daisy Hill Primary School
Daisy Hill
DH6 7AB

Dear Mr Zechariah,

Thank you for your letter. You must be very
busy in the temple but would you please write and
tell us what the angel said.

You see, some of the class don't really believe
in angels and think you must have been dreaming.
My dad does that when he's watching the football
on the telly—dreams his team has scored a goal.

Best wishes,

Sarah and 3G

P.S. I've just remembered that you won't know
what the telly is, so please don't read that bit.

**This time it was Sarah's turn to read
the letter from the old man.**

The Temple Court
Jerusalem

Dear Sarah,

Thank you for your letter.

Angels, young lady, do most certainly exist! They are God's messengers sent by him to give us important messages. Bearing football results to sleeping fathers is not one of their responsibilities!

The angel who visited me had a very important message for me and for my wife, Elizabeth.

'You are to have a son,' he said. 'His name is to be John. He will be a great man.'

It was at this point that I made a rather foolish mistake. I told the angel that I couldn't believe it. Both Elizabeth and I were far too old to have children. Gabriel was not pleased.

'Because you have doubted God,' he said, 'you will not be able to speak until this promise comes true.'

I could not speak a single word. I went outside to the people in the Court of the Israelites to bless them. But I had to make signs with my hands to try and tell them what had happened. When I finished in the temple I returned home to Elizabeth. It was not easy explaining to her about my meeting with the angel in the temple.

May the Lord bless you as he has blessed my wife and me,

Zechariah

'So he couldn't speak,' said Claire. 'Alex, you wouldn't like to go and annoy an angel, would you?'

The others laughed—apart from Alex, that is.

'So,' said Mr Green, ignoring the joke, 'I think we need to make sure we understand where we've got to in the story.

Zechariah, a priest, was struck dumb in the temple. He was told that his wife Elizabeth would have a rather special baby whom they were to call John.'

'Didn't Mary, Jesus' mother, go and visit Elizabeth?' asked Amy.

'That's right, she did,' said Mr Green. 'It was soon after Gabriel had told Mary that

she was going to be the mother of Jesus. Mary went to visit Elizabeth and stayed with her for about three months. In fact, she went home to Nazareth only a few weeks before Elizabeth's baby was born.'

'Can we write to Elizabeth,' asked Claire, 'and find out about it?'

And this is what Claire wrote…

Daisy Hill Primary School
Daisy Hill
DH6 7AB

Dear Elizabeth,

Your husband, Zechariah, has been very kind and written to tell us about the angel he met and how he couldn't talk afterwards. But we wanted to know about your baby.

Did he get called John like the angel said? Did you have a party after he was born? I help my mum look after my baby brother—apart from changing him, that is.

Best wishes,

Claire and 3G

Claire read Elizabeth's letter to 3G.

Hillview
Judea

Dear Claire,

HILL VIEW

Zechariah has told me about your letters and I'd love to tell you the rest of the story.

Like Zechariah, I found it very hard to believe that I would have a baby at my age. But the angel was right and soon I knew that I was going to have a child. Mary and I spent a very happy three months together. We talked about babies and how amazing it was that God had chosen us to be the mothers of both John and Jesus.

Mary went home, back to Nazareth, and I got ready for the birth of my baby. All went well and I had a beautiful little boy as the angel had promised. A week after he was born he was taken for the naming ceremony. Our relatives and friends wanted to call him after his father. Zechariah knew that was wrong but he couldn't tell them that the baby's name must be John.

Excuse me, but I shall have to go, as the baby is crying.

God's blessing go with you,

Elizabeth

'So we still don't know if the baby got his right name or not,' said Alex.

'When my baby brother was christened,' said Claire, 'my mum and dad had to say his name in church.'

'I think we need another letter to finish the story,' said Mr Green. 'Edward, will you please see if you can find out what happened?'

And this is what Edward wrote...

Daisy Hill Primary School
Daisy Hill
DH6 7AB

Dear Elizabeth,

Thank you for your letter and we hope that the baby is all right. You never told us if John got called John or not, or if Zechariah was able to talk again.

Please, please, try and find time to let us know.

Best wishes,

Edward and 3G

P.S. Did the angel come and tell everyone the baby's name?

Hillview
Judea

Dear Edward,

Thank you for your letter. I am sorry not to have finished the story but the baby seems to want feeding whenever he wakes up.

As I was telling you, all our friends and relations wanted to call the baby Zechariah after his father. Just as they were about to do so, my husband got a writing tablet and wrote these words: 'His name is John.' As soon as he wrote the name he could speak again. Everyone was amazed.

They were sure that this was God's doing.

So our son was called John after all. He grew up to serve God in a very special way. He taught people about the coming of Jesus.

May the Lord who blessed us bless you,

Elizabeth

19

'So it all worked out all right in the end, then,' said David. 'He got his right name after all.'

'And old Zechariah could talk again,' said Alex.

'Zechariah praised God in some words you can read in the Bible,' added Mr Green. '"You, my child," he said, "will be called a prophet of the Most High God. You will go ahead of the Lord to prepare his road for him, to tell his people that they will be saved by having their sins forgiven." He was telling everyone what John would do when he grew up.'

'Wasn't he called John the Baptist?' asked Amy.

'That's right,' said Mr Green. 'John was called "John the Baptist" because he baptized people who were really sorry for the things they had done wrong. He also baptized Jesus, but that's another story we'll look at later. Now I think it's time you finished off the picture of the temple.'

And that is what they did.

Trouble with the ites!

'About twelve hundred years before Jesus was born, things were not going very well for God's people—the Israelites,' said Mr Green. 'They were in the country that was called Canaan but so too were lots of their enemies. Most of their enemies had names that ended in "ites"! Let's have another look at our map.'

Mr Green pointed to Canaan on the map.

'Tell me some of the "ites",' he said.

'Ammon-ites,' said Claire.

'Amor-ites,' said Ben.

'Edom-ites,' said Sarah.

'Mosquitob-ites,' said Alex.

Everyone, including Mr Green, laughed.

'Try Moab-ites instead, Alex,' suggested Mr Green.

'And Midian-ites,' said Amy, 'but they were further away.'

'They were further away,' agreed Mr Green, 'but they still attacked the Israelites. In fact, it's the Midianites that we are going to be thinking about—but we need to know one or two other things first.'

Mr Green opened the class Bible and read some verses from the book in the Old Testament called Judges. You could look them up—they come from chapter 6 and start at verse 1.

'So it didn't look good for the Israelites,' said Mr Green, as he put the Bible down. 'The Israelites had done a lot of wrong things. They had forgotten that they were God's people, and the Midianite army invaded the country. I think we need to hear from someone who was there. His name is Gideon.'

'Sounds like the postman's going to be busy again!' said Alex.

'Quite right,' said Mr Green, 'and we've just got time to catch the post. Alex, I think it's your turn to write.'

And this is the letter that Alex wrote...

Daisy Hill Primary School
Daisy Hill
DH6 7AB

Dear Mr Gideon,

We have been talking about you in class.
Please will you tell us what things were like when
the Midianites took over your country?

Mr Green, our teacher, says it must have been
very hard.

Best wishes,

Alex and 3G

The House of Joash
Ophrah

HILL VIEW

Dear Alex,

Thank you for your letter. I'll do my best to put you all in the picture.

For the past seven years Canaan, our country, has been under the control of the Midianites. They are a hard and cruel people. They take all our sheep, cattle and donkeys. They take all our food and kill our soldiers.

We have had to live in caves in the hills. We try to grow wheat in the tiny fields in the mountains but even then the Midianites often find it. We are near starvation and are desperate. We need a leader who will bring our men together and lead them against the Midianites.

I will try to smuggle this letter out to you. I just hope the Midianites don't get hold of it.

Must stop—I hear soldiers coming.

Gideon

Alex read the letter to 3G. No one spoke for a few moments.

'So,' said Mr Green, 'now we know what things were like for Gideon and the Israelites. Driven to the hills, living in caves, with very little food. Not much hope either. But they were God's people and God had different ideas. Time for another letter, please. Sarah, will you write to Gideon and perhaps we'll find out what God had in mind.'

And this is what Sarah wrote...

Daisy Hill Primary School
Daisy Hill
DH6 7AB

Dear Mr Gideon,

   We are very worried about you. Our teacher says that God had plans for you all. Did God rescue you?

   Please write and tell us if you possibly can.

   Best wishes,

Sarah

27

The House of Joash
Ophrah

Dear Sarah,

God is good. He did have plans for us. What I didn't expect was that he had plans for ME!

One day I was threshing some wheat in our old winepress. This was so the Midianite soldiers wouldn't see what I was doing. Suddenly there was someone else with me. Not a man. An angel.

He had come to tell me that God wanted me to rescue my people from the Midianites. I asked him how. I mean, not only is our family the weakest of all of them, but I am the least important member of the family.

'You will do it because God will help you.'

I'm sorry to say that I didn't really believe it. Somehow you don't really expect God to choose you, do you?

Gideon

Sarah read Gideon's letter to 3G.

'So Gideon couldn't believe it was all happening,' said David. 'All this angel business, that is.'

'You're right, David, Gideon was having problems,' said Mr Green. 'He asked for some proof that this was God's doing. Perhaps if we write again he'll tell us what he did. Ben, your turn, I think.'

And this is what Ben wrote...

Daisy Hill Primary School
Daisy Hill
DH6 7AB

Dear Mr Gideon,

   Thank you for your last letter. It was very brave of you to smuggle it out to us.
   We have been wondering how you managed to get the proof that God would help you.
   Best wishes,

   Ben and 3G

The House of Joash
Ophrah

Dear Ben,

In answer to your letter, we often take food to the temple as a 'thank you' gift to God. So before I set off against all those Midianite soldiers, I decided to prepare a meal for the angel—just to see what would happen.

When I gave the meal to the angel he touched the meat and bread with a stick he was holding. Imagine my surprise when suddenly flames sprang up and burnt up the food. I was terrified. I had dared to ask God for proof.

Now I knew that God was with me. I sent messages to all the other tribes. Soon there were over thirty thousand men camped with me in the mountains. It was then that I got cold feet again. I asked for further proof that God was going to use me to rescue Israel.

Up in the mountains we get cold nights and there's always a lot of dew in the morning. I told God that I was putting out some wool. If there was dew only on the wool and not on the ground then I would know I must lead the soldiers into battle. Well, what do you think? The next morning the ground was dry but I wrang enough water out of the wool to fill a bowl! And then I did it again the next night—this time I asked for the wool to be dry and the ground wet. Next morning the wool was as dry as a bone and the ground soaking wet!

Now there was no question. I had to lead our soldiers into battle. Now I had to believe it.

Gideon

Ben read Gideon's letter to 3G.

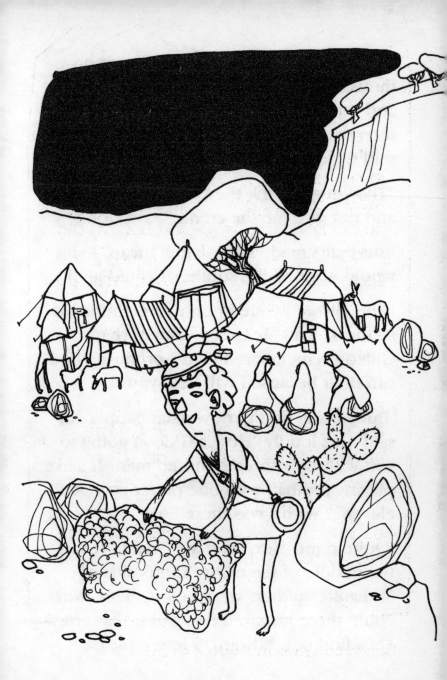

'So there was Gideon looking down on thousands of Midianite soldiers, their tents and their camels,' said Mr Green. 'It was then that God did a very strange thing. He told Gideon that he had too many soldiers.

"They might think they won by themselves and not give me the credit," said God.'

'But that's mad,' said Alex. 'I mean, I would want all the soldiers I could get!'

'God allowed Gideon only three hundred soldiers,' said Mr Green. 'But perhaps Gideon remembered God's promise, "You can do it because I will help you."'

'But we still don't know what happened,' said Alex loudly. 'How's Gideon going to win with only three hundred men? It's like playing football with one player against eleven. I wish I was there!'

'Quite right, Alex,' said Mr Green. 'It was the middle of the night. Thousands of Midianite soldiers were below them. What could three hundred do against that army? Let's find out. Edward, a letter, please.'

And this is what Edward wrote...

Daisy Hill Primary School
Daisy Hill
DH6 7AB

Dear Mr Gideon,

We can't wait to hear about the battle. Did you win?

Alex says he wishes he was there with you. He'd probably frighten off half the Midianites on his own!

Please write soon.

Edward and 3G
(desperate to know what happened)

The House of Joash
Ophrah

Dear Edward,

Yes! Praise God, we won.

Remember—it was very dark. Before
we went down the mountain I gave
strict orders to my soldiers. Each
was given a trumpet and a jar with a
torch in it. Silently we surrounded the
camp.

Just before midnight, when the
Midianites were sound asleep, we blew
our trumpets and broke the jars. We
shouted as loudly as we could, 'A
sword for the Lord and for Gideon!'
What happened was amazing. The
Midianites started to attack each
other. But most of them ran off as
fast as they could.

After all those years of hardship we
were free again.

The Lord is good.

Gideon

'Gideon lived for some time after that,' said Mr Green. 'Sadly, the Israelites didn't learn their lesson. They soon forgot God and started to worship other gods again. Even so, God gave them other leaders and, later on, a king. Now you have some work to do. Let's get those pictures finished and, Alex, I don't want to see a picture of you in the middle of the battle killing all the Midianites!'

A special moment

'What can you tell me about Jesus when he was young?' asked Mr Green one day.

The children in 3G thought for a moment.

'He was born in Bethlehem,' said Claire.

'Shepherds and wise men came to see him,' said Ben.

'Herod tried to kill him,' said David.

'Well done,' said Mr Green. 'And Joseph and Mary took the baby to Egypt until King Herod died.'

'But Jesus grew up in Nazareth, didn't he?' asked Hannah.

Mr Green nodded. 'Yes, when Herod died the family moved back to Nazareth, where Jesus grew up. The Bible tells us very little about Jesus as a child. But there is one story which we're going to look at. It happened when Jesus was twelve years old. I think we'll write another letter and find out about it. The best person to tell us would be Joseph. There's just time to catch the post. Who's going to write?'

'I think it's about my turn,' said Louise.

And this is what Louise wrote…

Daisy Hill Primary School
Daisy Hill
DH6 7AB

Dear Joseph,

We are trying to find out about when Jesus was young. Our teacher has told us that something special took place when Jesus was twelve years old.

Please write to us.

Yours sincerely,

Louise and 3G

Louise read the letter from Joseph to the class.

The Carpenter's Shop
Nazareth

Dear Louise,

Thank you for your letter. I shall be very pleased to tell you about Jesus.

When we heard that Herod had died, we went back home to Nazareth. Nazareth is a town in Galilee and I am one of the town's carpenters. We are a poor but happy family.

Jesus grew up quickly. He was always busy, always keen to learn. I taught him all I knew and his mother Mary did the same. He seemed especially interested when we went to the synagogue on the Sabbath. As he got older he began to prepare for his twelfth birthday when he would become a Son of the Law. According to Jewish custom this is when a boy becomes a man.

That year, Mary and I had a special surprise for Jesus. We were taking him to Jerusalem.

Must go now, as a customer has just come to collect a chair.

God's blessings,

Joseph

'So we know that Jesus became a Son of the Law when he was twelve,' said Mr Green. 'Today, Jews call the ceremony the bar-mitzvah. From then on he was expected to keep all the commandments of the Jewish law.'

'But Mr Green,' said Amy, 'Joseph said they had a surprise for Jesus. They were taking him to Jerusalem. Why was that so special?'

'We need to ask Joseph to explain that,' said Mr Green. 'Perhaps you'll write our next letter, Amy?'

And this is what Amy wrote…

Daisy Hill Primary School
Daisy Hill
DH6 7AB

Dear Joseph,

Thank you so much for your last letter. We were really interested to hear about Jesus growing up.

Please will you tell us why the visit to Jerusalem was so important.

Best wishes,

Amy and 3G

The Carpenter's Shop
Nazareth

Dear Amy,

I will try to explain why our visit to Jerusalem was so important for Jesus. You must remember that Jesus had just become a Son of the Law—he was now a man.

It is the responsibility of every Jewish man to visit Jerusalem at the Feast of Passover. Thousands come from near and far. The city is really crowded. Old friends greet old friends and there is a great atmosphere.

Jesus loved it. It was so unlike our quiet little town, with people from all over the world talking many different languages. But most of all it was his first visit to the temple, the site of so much of our history. Several times when we were there Jesus just sat in the temple court listening to all the talking that was going on.

Looking forward to your next letter.

May God bless you,

Joseph

'Jesus was taken by his parents to Jerusalem for the Feast of the Passover when he was twelve years old,' said Mr Green after Amy had read Joseph's letter. 'The Passover is very important to the Jewish people. It is a reminder of how God helped them escape from Egypt.'

Ben put up his hand.

'Why did they need to escape?' he asked.

'Because they were slaves and the Egyptians were very cruel to them,' said Mr Green. 'So Jesus was in Jerusalem at the Feast of Passover, visiting all the famous sites of the city, going to the temple and mixing with all those people. But it was soon time to go back to Nazareth. It was then that something very special happened. Time for another letter. I think Joseph is rather expecting it.'

And this is what David wrote…

Daisy Hill Primary School
Daisy Hill
DH6 7AB

Dear Joseph,

Thank you very much for your last letter. It must have been fantastic in Jerusalem with all those people.

Mr Green, our teacher, says that something happened on the way home. Please write and tell us about that.

Best wishes,

David and 3G

The Carpenter's Shop
Nazareth

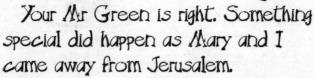

Dear David,

Your Mr Green is right. Something special did happen as Mary and I came away from Jerusalem.

There was a large group of us from Nazareth who had made the journey together—women, youngsters like Jesus, and the older men. Sometimes the youngsters walked with their mothers and sometimes they stayed with the men. The women left the city before the men—they walk more slowly, and we met up for the first overnight stop in the evening.

Mary was there but there was no sign of Jesus. I couldn't believe it. We were desperately worried. Mary thought he had come with me and I thought he had gone ahead with her. There was nothing for it but to go back and search in Jerusalem.

We looked in all the places we could think of—the markets, the shops, all the sites we had visited. And then after three days, almost when we had given up hope, we found Jesus in the temple. There he was, still sitting and listening and asking questions.

I should have thought about it before. He had been fascinated by the rabbis—our religious leaders. He had sat and listened to their talk and teaching. And there he was. Still sitting and listening and asking questions.

May God bless you,

Joseph

'I bet they were mad,' said Alex, after David had read Joseph's letter. 'I mean, my mum would've gone ballistic.'

'Mary and Joseph had spent a long time looking for Jesus. It must have been a bit of a surprise to find him in the temple,' said Mr Green. 'I wonder if it reminded them that Jesus was a very special boy? I wonder if Mary remembered the words of the angel who visited her before Jesus was born?'

'But that can't be the end of the story,' said Claire. 'They didn't just leave Jesus in Jerusalem, did they?'

'Write and find out, please, Claire,' said Mr Green.

And this is what Claire wrote…

Daisy Hill Primary School
Daisy Hill
DH6 7AB

Dear Joseph,

It must have been very worrying for you, losing Jesus like that. Did he get into trouble when you found him? Did he stay in Jerusalem or go home with you?

Please write and tell us.

Best wishes,

Claire and 3G

The Carpenter's Shop
Jerusalem

Dear Claire,

It was one of those very special moments when we met up with Jesus again. Mary said to Jesus, 'My son, why have you done this to us? Your father and I have been terribly worried trying to find you.'

I shall never forget what Jesus said.

'Why did you have to look for me? Didn't you know that I had to be in my Father's house?'

Jesus knew and I knew that he was talking about God and being in God's house. Our boy had grown into the special man the angel promised he would be. Nothing would ever be the same again from that moment.

But we went home, back to Nazareth. There Jesus grew into a fine, strong young man, preparing for what lay ahead. He was a good boy, did all we asked of him, and worked hard at learning the scriptures. But I never forgot seeing him in the temple. Somehow, he seemed to be at home there.

May God, the Father of Jesus, bless you,

Joseph

'And that is just about all we know about Jesus as a child,' said Mr Green. 'The next we hear about him is when he starts his work.'

Fish and chips!

'I'm going to give you a name,' said Mr Green to 3G, 'and I want you to tell me the first word that comes into your head.'

The children in 3G looked a bit puzzled. They hadn't played this game before.

'Right, we'll begin,' he said. 'Alan Shearer.'

Almost all the hands went up.

'Alex, you tell me your word.'

'Football,' said Alex. There was a loud cheer from some of the others.

'Roald Dahl,' said Mr Green.

'Books,' said Claire.

'Jonah,' said Mr Green.

'A whale!' said Ben.

'Almost right,' said Mr Green with a grin. 'Jonah did get swallowed by what the Bible says was a "large fish" and lots of people think it must have been a whale.'

'If he was swallowed by a large fish,' said

Alex, 'he must have had his chips!'

Everybody laughed.

'I mean, surely it must have killed him?' he asked.

'Actually, it didn't,' said Mr Green, 'but I think we had better start at the beginning of the story and not half way through.

Jonah was a prophet, which means he was somebody who told people about God and what God wanted them to do. He probably lived about eight hundred years or so before Jesus was born. I think it's time somebody wrote a letter to Jonah to find out how the story began. Edward, I think it's your turn.'

And this is what Edward wrote...

Daisy Hill Primary School
Daisy Hill
DH6 7AB

Dear Jonah,

Our teacher, Mr Green, has been telling us about your adventure with a large fish. It all sounds very exciting but we don't understand why you ended up in a fish's tummy. Please would you write and let us know how it all started?

Best wishes,

Edward and 3G

P.S. We have fish and chips at school on Fridays.

Ocean View
Joppa

Dear Edward and 3G,

Thank you for your letter regarding
my recent trip both above and below
the waves. It was a serious journey
with a very serious purpose.

One day God spoke to me and told
me to go to Nineveh. You can find
Nineveh quite easily on a map—it is
the capital city of the country called
Assyria. God told me that he knew
how wicked the people were there,
and he wanted me to tell them so.

Frankly, I wasn't keen on the job.
After all, Assyria is a deadly enemy
of my country, Israel. So I chickened
out. I went to the seaport of Joppa
and got on the first ship I could find
going in the opposite direction. As it
happened, it was a cargo ship going to
Spain. Some of you may have been
there on holiday. Well, I wasn't

exactly going on a cruise, as it turned out.

I boarded the ship and went down into the hold and fell asleep. Soon the wind got up and in next to no time there was a terrific storm. The ship was in danger of breaking up and the sailors were terrified. They threw the cargo overboard to make the ship lighter but even that made no difference.

The captain came and woke me up. He told me to pray to my God that we all might be saved. When the storm got even worse I confessed that I was running away from God. The sailors asked me what they should do to stop the storm. I told them that if they threw me into the sea it would all calm down.

I sounded a lot braver than I felt!
All best fishes,

Jonah

Edward read Jonah's letter to 3G.

'But he doesn't tell us anything about the "large fish",' complained Claire.

'No,' said Mr Green, 'there is a lot more of the story to come. But we have found out that God had a job for Jonah to do and he tried to run away without doing it.'

'Well, I'm going to write and find out about the fish,' said Claire.

And this is what she wrote…

Daisy Hill Primary School
Daisy Hill
DH6 7AB

Dear Jonah,

Thank you so much for your letter. We understand that you didn't go where God wanted you to go and that God made a big storm. Please tell us what happened next and where the big fish came into the story.

Best wishes,

Claire and 3G

Ocean View
Joppa

Dear Claire and 3G,

Thank you for your letter. I did rather leave the story unfinished in my last letter.

The sailors didn't want to see me drown. They tried hard to row the ship ashore but the wind was far too strong. So they prayed to God and then did what I had told them to do. They held my arms and threw me overboard into that boiling sea.

As soon as I hit the surface, the wind dropped. The sailors were amazed and began at once to praise my God and yours, the one true Lord.

As I started to sink I was sure that my last moment had come. Nothing could save me now. But with God all things are possible. He made a huge fish come and swallow me.

I lived inside that fish for three whole days.

It was then that I prayed to God as I had never prayed before. You might like to read what I said. You'll find it in chapter 2 of the book named after me in the Old Testament.

But my story doesn't end there. God wanted me to do something more useful than being fish food! Let me know if you want to find out what happened.

May the Lord keep you from all danger,

Jonah

'Well, we do want to know what happened! I mean, did he stay in the fish?' asked Claire when she had read the letter to 3G.

'No, he didn't,' said Mr Green. 'God had something special for Jonah to do. So let's find out if Jonah did it. Will you write, David, please?'

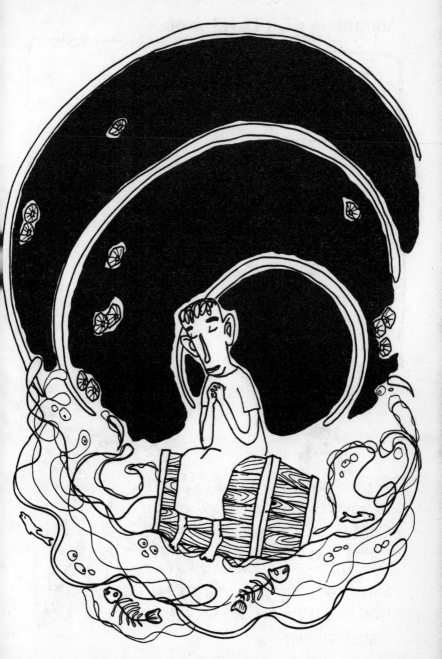

63

And this is what David wrote...

Daisy Hill Primary School
Daisy Hill
DH6 7AB

Dear Jonah,

   We were so pleased that you were saved from drowning. It must have been awfully smelly inside that fish.

   We think you got out and went to Nineveh after all. Are we right?

   Best wishes from David and 3G

Ocean View
Joppa

Dear David and 3G,

Yes, you are right. I was in the fish for three days and then it spat me out on to dry land. The first thing I had was a good wash! It was then that God spoke to me again.

'Go to Nineveh,' said God, 'and give them my message.'

Nineveh was enormous—it was so big, it would have taken three days to walk right through it. At the end of one day's walk I spoke to the people.

'In forty days your city will be destroyed,' I told them.

The result was incredible. Everybody was sorry they had behaved so badly. They put on sackcloth instead of their designer clothes and even the king sat down in ashes, rather than on his throne. This was to show how sorry he was for the things his people had done wrong.

The king ordered his people to pray to God and give up their bad behaviour.

'Perhaps God will change his mind; perhaps he will stop being angry, and we will not die,' said the king.

And that was what happened. God saw they had changed and he did not punish them. It was then that I threw a major wobbly. I knew all along this was what would happen. In fact I had told God right at the beginning that this was what he would do.

I was so fed up with the whole thing that I asked God to let me die.

Well, that's enough of my troubles.

Jonah

As David read Jonah's letter his face got longer and longer.

'Oh dear,' he said, 'I do hope he's all right. He sounds really sick.'

'Jonah at last had done what God wanted,'

said Mr Green. 'He went to Nineveh and told all the people that God would destroy their city. The people listened to Jonah and changed their ways. God listened to their prayers and changed his mind. And Jonah said to God, "I told you so. I know you are a loving God, ready to forgive people." When all this happened Jonah went into a super sulk. Bit like some of you when I give you a lot of homework!'

'But surely the story doesn't end with Jonah in a sulk?' asked Sarah.

'You're right, Sarah,' said Mr Green, 'and you can write our last letter, so Jonah can tell you the end of his whale of a story.'

3G groaned loudly. Sarah picked up her pen and this is what she wrote...

Daisy Hill Primary School
Daisy Hill
DH6 7AB

Dear Jonah,

Thank you very much for your last letter. We have been very worried about you and hope you are feeling better.

Please tell us how the story ended.

All best wishes,

Sarah and 3G

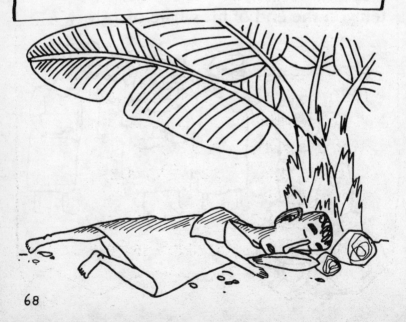

Ocean View
Joppa

Dear Sarah and 3G,

Thanks for your letter. Yes, I have calmed down a bit now. You see, God taught me yet another lesson.

After I told God I might as well die, I stormed out of Nineveh, made myself a shelter and sat down in its shade to see what God would do about Nineveh. In next to no time God made a really big plant grow just by me. It had huge leaves and kept the sun off. I loved that plant.

When I woke up the next day, the plant was dead. A worm had eaten the roots. I was boiling mad again.

'What right have you to be angry over the plant?' asked God.

'Every right,' I said. 'I'm angry enough to die!'

'But,' said God, 'you didn't do anything for it, you didn't make it grow. And yet you felt sorry for it. How much more than that should I feel sorry for the people in Nineveh!'

As usual, God was right. He is a loving and kind God. He forgave them and he forgave me.

Remember me when you see a big fish.

Best wishes,

Jonah

Sarah read Jonah's last letter to 3G.

'What a story!' said Alex.

'Fintastic,' said Edward.

'Jonah was the first person to take God's message to people who were not Jews,' said Mr Green. 'He was really the first missionary.'

Paul and the wall

'One of the most amazing people in the Bible is Paul,' said Mr Green. 'He had more adventures in a year than most people have in a lifetime. Does anyone know where we can read about Paul in the Bible?'

Not one hand went up. The children in 3G just looked at each other.

'It's in the Acts of the Apostles,' said Mr Green. 'The Acts of the Apostles is the book that comes right after the four gospels—Matthew, Mark, Luke, John, and then Acts. It's the story of what happened on earth after Jesus returned to heaven. It was also written by Luke.'

Mr Green showed 3G where Acts was in the big class Bible.

'Most of Jesus' friends were still in Jerusalem. A lot of the Jewish leaders were getting very worried. You see, they thought that when Jesus died that would be the end of it. But now it seemed that more and more people were believing that

71

Jesus was the Son of God. And the Jewish leaders didn't like that at all. And that was where Paul came into it.'

'But I thought that Paul was on the Christian side,' said Alex.

'Well, let's write some more letters and find out,' said Mr Green. 'We'll start at the beginning of Paul's story. This means writing to the High Priest in the temple in Jerusalem. Edward, I think it's your turn.'

And this is what Edward wrote…

Daisy Hill Primary School
Daisy Hill
DH6 7AB

Dear Your Holiness,

We are hoping that you will be able to help us. We are trying to find out about a man named Paul. We were surprised to hear that he wanted to catch all the followers of Jesus and put them in prison. Do you remember him?

Yours sincerely,

Edward and Class 3G

The House of the High Priest
Jerusalem

Dear Edward,

I have been asked to reply to your letter by my master, the High Priest. Whilst he thanks you for your letter he wishes to have nothing to do with the traitor known as Paul.

There have been many rumours about Jesus returning to life again. Obviously this is quite impossible. It was Paul's task to round up the followers of Jesus to prevent such rumours spreading.

Paul, so we are informed, behaved very strangely as he got close to Damascus. He claimed to have seen a bright light and heard a voice. We think it was the sun. It can be very hot at this time of the year.

May the God of our fathers bless you,

Reuben
Scribe to the High Priest

'So,' said Mr Green after Edward had read the letter to the class, 'the High Priest wants nothing more to do with Paul.'

'He got quite shirty over it, didn't he?' said Alex.

'Not really surprising, I suppose,' said Mr Green. 'One minute Paul is chasing Christians and the next minute he has become one! It must have come as a shock to the High Priest.'

'But how do we find out what happened?' asked Claire.

'I think the answer to that is to write to the man himself,' said Mr Green. 'Claire, will you please write a letter now to Paul?'

And this is what Claire wrote...

Daisy Hill Primary School
Daisy Hill
DH6 7AB

Dear Paul,

We have been trying to find out what happened to you on the way to Damascus. The High Priest won't help us. If you're not too busy, please let us know.

Best wishes,

Claire and 3G

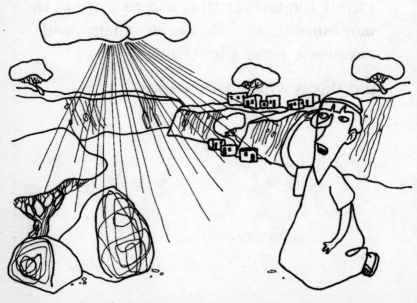

Tent Makers Ltd
Tarsus

Dear Claire,

Thank you for your letter. I would love to tell you about meeting Jesus outside Damascus.

You probably know that I thought the Christians were wrong to follow Jesus and to believe that he was the Son of God. Just outside Damascus the most amazing thing happened. I could see the city ahead of me and was looking forward to getting on with my work. Suddenly there was a very bright light. I fell to the ground and heard a voice asking me a question.

'Why do you persecute me?' said the voice.

'Who are you, Lord?' I asked.

'I am Jesus, whom you persecute,' said the voice.

Jesus ordered me to go into Damascus. When I got up from the ground I couldn't see a thing. I was led by the hand to a house in the city. There in the darkness I prayed and waited for what God would do next.

Yours faithfully,

Paul

'Wow!' said Alex, when they read Paul's letter. 'It's excellent. I mean, there he was chasing Christians when suddenly all this happens.'

'But surely Paul didn't stay not being able to see?' asked Amy.

'No, he didn't,' said Mr Green. 'God had a lot of work for Paul to do. And I've got some work for you to do. Before we go any further, let's draw Paul on his way to Damascus.'

The children worked hard at their drawings and Mr Green pinned them up on the wall.

'I think we need another letter to see how things worked out. How about you, Ben? This time, though, I want you to write to a man called Ananias. He is a Christian who lives in Damascus. I think he might help us to find out how Paul got his sight back.'

And this is what Ben wrote…

Daisy Hill Primary School
Daisy Hill
DH6 7AB

Dear Mr Ananias,

We are trying to find out what happened to Paul in Damascus. We know that he was blind when he came into the city. We think that you met Paul and helped him.

You must have been a bit frightened because Paul was chasing Christians.

Please write and tell us what happened.

Best wishes,

Ben and 3G

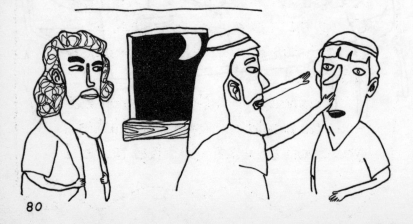

The Followers of the Way
Damascus

Dear Ben,

Thank you for your letter asking about Paul.

You are quite right. I was terrified about meeting Paul.

I had heard about the terrible things he had done to the Christians in Jerusalem. God told me in a dream to visit him. I DIDN'T WANT TO GO! But God, as always, knew best and I went.

My knees were knocking as I walked down Straight Street. I found Paul, just as God had told me, in Judas' house. He was a changed man. There was no doubt now that he loved Jesus and wanted to become a Christian.

I touched him with my hands and at once he could see again. With his eyes open to what God had done, I baptized him in the name of Jesus. Almost at once he started telling people about Jesus He told everyone that Jesus was the Son of God.

You can imagine how surprised everybody was.

'He was the one who killed those who believed in Jesus,' they said.

'Yes, he was going to take them back to the chief priests. Now look at him!'

Of course, this was stirring up real trouble. I think you should ask Paul about his next adventures.

Keep following the Way,

Ananias

'He was really brave, that Ananias,' said Louise. 'I wouldn't have fancied going to see Paul.'

'He certainly was,' agreed Mr Green. 'It must have been very hard for the Christians in Damascus to believe that Paul had changed so much. But then Paul was very brave speaking in the synagogues.'

'I reckon some of his old friends were out to get him now,' said David. 'I don't think his chances were good in Damascus!'

'So let's find out from Paul himself,' said Mr Green. 'Louise, I think it's your turn to write.'

And this is what Louise wrote…

Daisy Hill Primary School
Daisy Hill
DH6 7AB

Dear Paul,

We really, really want to know how things went in Damascus after you started telling people about Jesus. We reckon some of your old friends would have been pretty unhappy with the way things were going.

Please write and let us know.

Yours sincerely,

Louise and 3G

Tent Makers Ltd
Tarsus

Dear Louise,

Thanks for your letter asking about my time in Damascus.

The more I told people about Jesus, the angrier the leaders of the synagogues became. I had become a Christian. I was now one of those I used to put in prison for what they believed.

One day I heard, by the grace of God, that the Jewish leaders in Damascus were planning to kill me. Men were watching day and night at the gates of the city in case I tried to leave. I had to get out. God had more for me to do. And then one of my new friends had a brilliant idea.

One very dark night I climbed into a big wicker basket, the sort used to carry food to the market. My friends checked to see nobody was about and then gently lowered the basket out of an opening in the city wall. I had escaped!

I made my way safely back to Jerusalem—a very different person from the one who had come to Damascus a few months before. The chaser had become the chased!

But there were still problems ahead. If you want to know more, I suggest you write to my friend Barnabas.

May God bless you,

Paul

'It wasn't easy being a Christian in those days,' said Mr Green. 'Paul was a very brave man. No sooner did he escape from Damascus than he went to Jerusalem. If he was a wanted man in Damascus he was even more so in Jerusalem.'

'It seems like a funny thing to do,' said Alex. 'I mean, he could have been caught in Jerusalem and put into prison with all those Christians he had arrested.'

'I think what he needed to do was to meet the main Christian leaders like Peter and John. He risked his life going to Jerusalem. I wonder what happened when he got there? I think we need another letter, but this time to Barnabas, as Paul suggested.'

'It's my turn,' said David.

And this is what David wrote…

Daisy Hill Primary School
Daisy Hill
DH6 7AB

Dear Barnabas,

We are trying to find out what happened when Paul came back to Jerusalem from Damascus. We know that he had to escape from Damascus. Was he safe in Jerusalem?

Best wishes,

David and 3G

P.S. Paul said we should write to you.

David read Barnabas' letter to 3G. They listened hard.

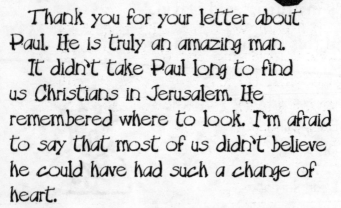

The Upper Room
Jerusalem

Dear David,

Thank you for your letter about Paul. He is truly an amazing man.

It didn't take Paul long to find us Christians in Jerusalem. He remembered where to look. I'm afraid to say that most of us didn't believe he could have had such a change of heart.

After some days I decided to speak to him. We met secretly and he told me how he had met Jesus on the road to Damascus. He told me how he had been telling people about Jesus and how he had had to escape from the city.

There was no doubt in my mind. God had changed him. The others were frightened. They thought this might be a trick. I took Paul to the apostles, told them what he had told me, and they were convinced. Paul stayed with us and at once started to tell everyone in Jerusalem about Jesus.

But that was only the beginning. Once again his life was in danger. If you want to know more about this amazing man, then read Luke's book.

God bless you all,

Barnabas

'So Paul got to Jerusalem,' said Mr Green, 'and met the apostles, the really close friends of Jesus. He started to tell people about Jesus but his life was in danger. He went home to Tarsus but it wasn't long before his adventures started again.'

'Well, I never thought the Bible could be so exciting,' said Alex.

'Now we'll make our own books about Paul. You can decide which picture you want to put on the front,' said Mr Green.

And that is what they did.

Bible references and suggestions of ways to use this book

The Bible references for each chapter are listed on page 92. They are there to enable any parent or teacher to look at the wider context of the passages actually incorporated in the story and thus to explain or expand on the situation.

The references are also given with the hope that where there is opportunity they will be looked up with the children or child. This is an important aspect of finding the way around the Bible and learning more of the whole.

In some stories references are made in the text to specific Bible passages where, for instance, Mr Green has read a passage to the children in class. It would be very helpful to read these passages as they occur within the stories.

Look out for another book in the 'Just time to catch the post' series.

Can we have a party?

Writing letters can be exciting—you never quite know what sort of reply you're going to get—as the children in 3G discovered when they decided to drop a line to a shepherd called Nathan. After all, they *did* want to know what happened when the angels turned up on that first Christmas Eve.

The more they found out, the more questions there were to be answered!

Sarah wanted to know why Hannah was so unhappy on the day she went into the temple at Shiloh. Amy wanted to know why Lostson left home. David wanted to know why Mr Green said that the book of Ruth was a love story. And Claire wanted to know what happened to the man who was attacked as he travelled from Jerusalem to Jericho.

With pens poised and paper at the ready, there was just time to catch the post!

ISBN 1 84101 050 2, £3.99

Available from your local bookshop or, in case of difficulty, contact BRF on 01865 748227.